AVALON HIGH
CORONATION

AVALON HIGH
CORONATION

VOLUME 1:
THE MERLIN PROPHECY

CREATED AND WRITTEN BY
MEG CABOT

ILLUSTRATED BY
JINKY CORONADO

TOKYOPOP®

HAMBURG // LONDON // LOS ANGELES // TOKYO

HarperCollinsPublishers

Avalon High: Coronation vol. 1
Created and Written by Meg Cabot
Illustrated by Jinky Coronado

Associate Editor - Kathy Schilling
Lettering - Lucas Rivera
Cover Design - James Lee

Editor - Julie Taylor
Digital Imaging Manager - Chris Buford
Pre-Production Supervisor - Erika Terriquez
Art Director - Anne Marie Horne
Production Manager - Elisabeth Brizzi
Managing Editor - Vy Nguyen
VP of Production - Ron Klamert
Editor-in-Chief - Rob Tokar
Publisher - Mike Kiley
President and C.O.O. - John Parker
C.E.O. and Chief Creative Officer - Stuart Levy

Acknowledgments
Many, many thanks to Jinky Coronado, Laura Langlie,
Amanda Maciel, Julie Taylor, and the entire team at TokyoPop.

A Manga

TOKYOPOP and 🐢 are trademarks or registered trademarks of TOKYOPOP Inc.

TOKYOPOP Inc.
5900 Wilshire Blvd. Suite 2000
Los Angeles, CA 90036

E-mail: info@TOKYOPOP.com
Come visit us online at www.TOKYOPOP.com

Library of Congress Cataloging-in-Publication Data
Cabot, Meg.
   The Merlin prophecy / by Meg Cabot. — 1st HarperTeen ed.
      p. cm. — (Avalon High ; bk. 1)
ISBN 978-0-06-145944-3
1. Graphic novels. I. Title.
PN6727.C23M47 2007   2007006987
741.5'973—dc22

1 2 3 4 5 6 7 8 9 10
❖
First Edition

For Benjamin

ONE SMALL BAND OF LOYAL SUPPORTERS--
THE ORDER OF THE BEAR--BELIEVED THAT
THIS KING--THE NOBLE ARTHUR--WOULD
RISE AGAIN, TO LEAD OUR WORLD FROM
THE DARKNESS INTO THE LIGHT.

FOR NEARLY FIFTEEN
HUNDRED YEARS,

THESE BELIEVERS
HAVE WAITED,

ONLY TO SEE
THEIR HOPES
DASHED AGAIN...

...AND AGAIN.

MY NAME IS ELLIE HARRISON, AND MY WORLD CIV TEACHER, MR. MORTON (OR MERLIN--AT LEAST, ACCORDING TO THE ORDER OF THE BEAR), TRULY BELIEVES THIS...AND HAS MY MEDIEVAL HISTORIAN PARENTS BELIEVING IT, TOO.

IN MY OPINION, WILL IS THE REINCARNATION OF KING ARTHUR.

HMM...

ALL OF WHICH IS FINE BY ME, BECAUSE IT JUST MEANS I GET TO SPEND MORE TIME THAN EVER WITH WILL.

13

BASICALLY, THE ORDER OF THE BEAR IS MADE UP OF A BUNCH OF HISTORIANS AND SCHOLARS WHO HAVE HELD ON TO THE BELIEF THAT ARTHUR WOULD SOMEDAY BE REINCARNATED...

...AND LEAD THE WORLD INTO A NEW AGE OF PEACE AND ENLIGHTENMENT, LIKE THE ONE THAT OCCURRED BACK WHEN CAMELOT EXISTED.

WHICH YOU WOULD THINK EVERYONE WANTS, RIGHT? WELL, SURPRISINGLY, NOT SO MUCH, IT TURNS OUT.

TAKE WILL'S HALF-BROTHER, MARCO, FOR INSTANCE.

MARCO WASN'T TOO JAZZED WHEN WILL AND I HOOKED UP. OH, NOT BECAUSE MARCO WAS JEALOUS. AT LEAST, NOT OF ME.

WILL, I HAVE SOMETHING TO TELL YOU. YOU'RE MY FULL-BLOODED SON, NOT MY STEPSON.

WHAT?

23

MARCO WASN'T TOO HAPPY WHEN HE FOUND OUT HIS MOM, WHO'D JUST MARRIED WILL'S DAD--IN SPITE OF THE FACT THAT THE ADMIRAL COMMANDED THE MILITARY UNIT IN WHICH HER FIRST HUSBAND, MARCO'S FATHER, WAS KILLED--WAS ACTUALLY WILL'S REAL MOM, WHOM WILL HAD ALWAYS BEEN TOLD WAS DEAD.

CERTAINLY MR. MORTON BELIEVES IT.

JUST LIKE HE BELIEVES THAT JENNIFER, WILL'S EX-GIRLFRIEND, COULDN'T HELP FALLING FOR LANCE, WILL'S BEST FRIEND--ANY MORE THAN GUINEVERE COULD HELP FALLING FOR LANCELOT...

I HONESTLY DON'T KNOW HOW MUCH OF THAT IS TRUE. BUT I DO KNOW HOW LUCKY I AM. I MEAN, IS THERE ANY OTHER HIGH SCHOOL GIRL YOU KNOW WHO BASICALLY GETS TO LIVE WITH--EVEN IF IT'S ONLY PLATONICALLY...MUCH TO MY EVERLASTING CHAGRIN, WILL BEING TOO NOBLE TO MAKE A MOVE ON THE DAUGHTER OF THE PEOPLE WHO SO KINDLY TOOK HIM IN WHEN HIS OWN PARENTS THREW HIM OUT-- HER BOYFRIEND AND POSSIBLE REINCARNATION OF KING ARTHUR?

GOOD NIGHT.

GOOD NIGHT.

G'NIGHT, YOU TWO.

RUFF!

35

CHAPTER TWO

ESPECIALLY SINCE MARCO IS SAFELY LOCKED AWAY IN A PRIVATE MENTAL HOSPITAL AT HIS PARENTS' EXPENSE. AS WILL OFTEN POINTS OUT TO ME.

I MEAN, IT'S BEEN OVER TWO MONTHS SINCE ALL OF THAT HAPPENED. I SHOULD BE OVER IT BY NOW. I KNOW WILL IS. WELL, EXCEPT FOR THE FACT THAT HE HASN'T SEEN HIS MOM IN SO LONG...

CRUNCH

AND HOW CAN I GET
WILL TO DO THE SAME?

CHAPTER THREE

WOW, YOU'RE REALLY TAKING THIS DRESS SHOPPING THING SERIOUSLY.

YOU HAVEN'T SAID A WORD IN TEN MINUTES.

SORRY, I WAS JUST THINKING ABOUT SOME-THING ELSE.

JUST WAIT.

WHY DO I FEEL SCARED NOW?

CHAPTER FOUR

SHE KNOWS THAT, WILL. SHE FEELS AWFUL ABOUT IT.

THAT'S WHY WE DECIDED WE SHOULD ALL GET TOGETHER FOR DINNER. YOU AND ME AND YOUR PARENTS AND MY PARENTS... SO WE CAN CLEAR THE AIR--

WAIT--WHEN DID *WE* DECIDE THIS?

TODAY. AT THE MALL. WHAT'S WRONG?

For all the books about Ellie and more by

MEG CABOT

check out the following pages!

You'll find:

- More about *Avalon High*, the novel!
- Blurbs about Meg's other exciting books
- Info about the Princess Diaries series

Still not enough?
For even more about Meg Cabot, go to

www.harperteen.com/megcabot

You can read Meg's online diary,
find the latest info on her books,
take quizzes, and win fabulous prizes!

Ellie has a hunch that nothing is as it seems in

AVALON HIGH

Avalon High seems like a typical school, with typical students. There's Lance, the jock. Jennifer, the cheerleader. And Will, senior class president, quarterback, and all-around good guy. But not everyone at Avalon High is who they appear to be . . . not even, as new student Ellie is about to discover, herself. What part does she play in the drama that is unfolding? What if the chain of coincidences she has pieced together means—like the court of King Arthur—tragedy is fast approaching Avalon High? Worst of all, what if there's nothing she can do about it?

From

AVALON HIGH

I got out of the car and did a few stretches while I surreptitiously watched my dad prepare for his run. He'd put away his wire rims—he's blind as a bat without them. In fact, in medieval times, he'd probably have been dead by the age of three or four from falling down a well or whatever; I'd inherited my mom's twenty-twenty vision, so most likely I'd have lived a bit longer—and put on these thick plastic-rimmed glasses that have an elastic band he can snap behind his head to keep them from sliding off while he runs. Mom calls this his Dork Strap.

"This is a nice running path," my dad was saying, as he adjusted his Dork Strap. Unlike me, who'd spent hours in the pool, Dad wasn't a bit tan. His legs were the color of notebook paper. Only with hair. "It's exactly one mile per lap. It goes through some woods—a kind of arboretum—over there. See? So it's not all in the hot sun. There's some shade."

I slid my headphones on. I can't run without music, except during meets, when they won't let you. I find that rap is ideal for running. The angrier the rapper, the better. Eminem is ideal to listen to while running, because he's so mad at everyone. Except his daughter.

"Two laps?" I asked my dad.

"Sure," he said.

And so I turned on my iPod mini—I keep it on an arm strap when I run, which is different than a Dork Strap—and started running.

It was hard at first. It's more humid in Maryland than it is back home, I guess on account of the sea. The air is actually heavy. It's like running through soup.

But after a while, my joints seemed to loosen up. I started remembering how much I'd liked to run back home. It's hard and everything. Don't get me wrong. But I like how strong and powerful my legs feel underneath me while I run . . . like I can do anything. Anything at all.

There was hardly anyone else on the path—just old ladies, mostly, power-walking with their dogs—but I tore past them, leaving them in my wake. I didn't smile as I ran by. Back home, everybody smiles at strangers. Here, the only time people smile is if you smile first. It didn't take my parents very long to catch on to this. Now they make me smile—and even wave—at everyone we pass. Especially our new neighbors, when they're out in their yards mowing their lawns or whatever. Image, my mom calls it. It's important to keep up a good image, she says. So people won't think we're snobs.

Except that I'm not really sure I care what people around here think about me.

The running path started out like a normal track, with closely cut grass on either side of it, snaking between the baseball diamond and the lacrosse field, then curving past the dog runs and around the parking lot.

Then it left the grass behind, and disappeared into a surprisingly thick forest. Yeah, a real forest, right in the middle of nowhere, with a discreet little brown sign that said WELCOME TO THE ANNE ARUNDEL COUNTY ARBORETUM by the side of the path.

I was a little shocked, as I ran past the sign, at how wild the undergrowth on either side of the trail had been allowed to get. Plunging into the deep shade of the arboretum, I noticed that the leaves overhead were so thick, hardly any sunlight at all was allowed to get through.

Still, the vegetation on either side of me was lush and prickly looking. I was sure there was also a ton of poison ivy in there, too . . . something that, if you contracted it badly enough back in medieval times, could probably have killed you, since there wasn't any cortisone.

You could barely see two feet beyond the path, the brambles and trees were so close together. But it was at least ten degrees cooler in the arboretum than it was in the rest of the park. The shade cooled the sweat that was dripping down my face and chest. It was hard to believe, running through that thick wood, that I was still near civilization. But when I pulled out my headphones to listen, I could hear cars going by on the highway beyond the thick growth of trees.

Which was kind of a relief. You know, that I hadn't accidentally gotten lost in Jurassic Park, or whatever.

I plopped my earphones back into place and kept going. I was breathing really hard now, but I still felt good. I couldn't hear my feet striking the path—I could only hear the music in my ears—but it seemed to me for a minute that I was the only person in these woods . . . maybe the only person in the whole world.

Which was ridiculous, since I knew my dad wasn't that far behind me—probably not going much faster than the power-walking ladies, but behind me nonetheless.

Still, I had seen too many TV movies where the heroine was jogging innocently along and some random psychopath comes popping out of thick growth, just like the stuff on either side of me, and attacks her. I wasn't taking any chances. Who knew what kind of freaks were lurking? I mean, it was Annapolis, home of the U.S. Naval Academy and the capital of Maryland, and all—hardly an area known for harboring violent criminals.

But you never know.

Good thing my legs were so strong. If someone did jump out at me from the trees, I was pretty confident that I could deliver a good kick to his head. And keep stomping on him until help came.

It was right as I was thinking this that I saw him.

A hilarious new novel about getting in trouble, getting caught, and getting the guy!

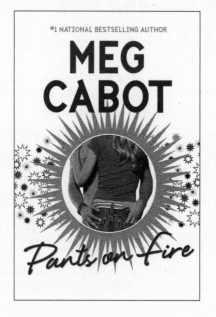

Katie Ellison has everything going for her senior year—a great job, two boyfriends, and a good shot at being crowned Quahog Princess of her small coastal town in Connecticut. So why does Tommy Sullivan have to come back into her life? Sure, they used to be friends, but that was before the huge screwup that turned their whole town against him. Now he's back, and making Katie's perfect life a total disaster. Can the Quahog Princess and the *freak* have anything in common? Could they even be falling for each other?

HARPER TEEN
An Imprint of HarperCollins Publishers

www.harperteen.com

the mediator

Suze can see ghosts. Which is kind of a pain most of the time, but when Suze moves to California and finds Jesse, the ghost of a nineteenth-century hottie haunting her bedroom, things begin to look up.

THE MEDIATOR 1:

Shadowland

THE MEDIATOR 2:

Ninth Key

THE MEDIATOR 3:

Reunion

THE MEDIATOR 4:

Darkest Hour

THE MEDIATOR 5:

Haunted

THE MEDIATOR 6:

Twilight

ALL-AMERICAN

What if you were going about your average life when all of a sudden, you accidentally saved the president's life? Oops! This is exactly what happens to Samantha Madison while she's busy eating cookies and rummaging through CDs. Suddenly her life as a sophomore in high school, usually spent pining after her older sister's boyfriend or living in the academic shadows of her younger sister's genius, is sent spinning. Now everyone at school—and in the country!—seems to think Sam is some kind of hero. Everyone, that is, except herself. But the number-one reason Samantha Madison's life has gone completely insane is that, on top of all this . . . the president's son just might be in love with her!

Ready OR Not

In this sequel to *All-American Girl*, everyone thinks Samantha Madison—who, yes, DID save the president's life—is ready: Her parents think she's ready to learn the value of a dollar by working part-time, her art teacher thinks she's ready for "life drawing" (who knew that would mean "naked people"?!), the president thinks she's ready to make a speech on live TV, and her boyfriend (who just happens to be David, the president's son) seems to think they're ready to take their relationship to the Next Level. . . .

The only person who's not sure Samantha Madison is ready for any of the above is Samantha herself!

*Girl-next-door Jenny Greenley goes stir-crazy
(or star-crazy?) in Meg Cabot's*

TEEN IDOL

Jenny Greenley's good at solving problems—so good she's the school paper's anonymous advice columnist. But when nineteen-year-old screen sensation Luke Striker comes to Jenny's small town to research a role, he creates havoc that even level-headed Jenny isn't sure she can repair . . . especially since she's right in the middle of all of it. Can Jenny, who always manages to be there for everybody else, learn to take her own advice, and find true love at last?

Does Steph have what it takes?

HOW TO BE Popular

Everyone wants to be popular—or at least, Stephanie Landry does. Steph's been the least popular girl in her class since a certain cherry Super Big Gulp catastrophe five years earlier. And she's determined to get in with the It Crowd this year—no matter what! After all, Steph's got a secret weapon: an old book called—what else?—*How to Be Popular.*

Turns out . . . it's easy to become popular. What isn't so easy? Staying that way!

Finally, don't miss these
two irresistible love stories!

Nicola and the Viscount

It's only her first London Season, but sixteen-year-old Nicola has made up her mind: Handsome, charming, poetry-reading Lord Sebastian is, simply, a god. So when the divine viscount starts paying special attention to her, Nicola is certain she's found her destiny.

Everything is perfect until the infuriating—and disturbingly handsome—Nathaniel Sheridan begins to cast doubt on the viscount's character . . . and on Nicola's feelings.

Victoria and the Rogue

Wealthy young heiress Lady Victoria Arbuthnot is accustomed to handling her own affairs—and everyone else's. So when she's suddenly sent to London to find a husband, Victoria quickly finds a perfect English gentleman.

Everything is just as she wants it—that is, if the raffish young ship captain Jacob Carstairs would stop meddling in her plans.

READ ALL OF THE BOOKS ABOUT MIA!

The Princess Diaries

THE PRINCESS DIARIES, VOLUME II:
Princess in the Spotlight

THE PRINCESS DIARIES, VOLUME III:
Princess in Love

THE PRINCESS DIARIES, VOLUME IV:
Princess in Waiting

Valentine Princess
A PRINCESS DIARIES BOOK (VOLUME IV AND A QUARTER)

THE PRINCESS DIARIES, VOLUME IV AND A HALF:
Project Princess

THE PRINCESS DIARIES, VOLUME V:
Princess in Pink

THE PRINCESS DIARIES, VOLUME VI:
Princess in Training

The Princess Present:
A PRINCESS DIARIES BOOK (VOLUME VI AND A HALF)

THE PRINCESS DIARIES, VOLUME VII:
Party Princess

Sweet Sixteen Princess:
A PRINCESS DIARIES BOOK (VOLUME VII AND A HALF)

THE PRINCESS DIARIES, VOLUME VIII:
Princess on the Brink

ILLUSTRATED BY CHESLEY McLAREN

Princess Lessons:
A PRINCESS DIARIES BOOK

Perfect Princess:
A PRINCESS DIARIES BOOK

Holiday Princess:
A PRINCESS DIARIES BOOK

But wait!
There's more by Meg: